WHAT A MONSTER!

Contents

Haydn Middleton

Story illustrated by
Rory Walker

Find out about

- Make-believe monsters from myths!

Tricky words

- cruel
- huge
- humans
- lizard
- eagle
- treasure

Introduce these tricky words and help the reader when they come across them later!

Text starter

Take a look at these monsters. Some are like humans. Some are like animals. Some are like a horrible mix of humans *and* animals! Read about the cruel centaur, cyclops and the Minotaur.

Make-Believe Monsters

Centaur (say *sen-tor*)

A centaur is half a man and half a horse.

Centaurs can be kind but some centaurs are very cruel.

Cyclops (say *sy-clops*)

A cyclops is a giant who has just one huge eye.

They are very cruel.
They like to eat humans.

Dragon

A dragon has a body like a huge lizard with wings.

Dragons can be very cruel. They eat humans and steal their treasure.

Dragons can breathe fire!

Would you like to meet a griffin?

Griffin

A griffin has the head and wings of an eagle and the body and legs of a lion. Griffins like to steal treasure.

Hydra (say *high-dra*)

The Hydra is a huge water snake.
It has lots of heads.

If a human chops off one of the
heads, *two* more heads grow!

Medusa (say *med-you-sir*)
Medusa has a human head
but her hair is made of snakes.

Her eyes are very cruel.
She can turn humans into stone.

Minotaur (say *my-no-tor*)

The Minotaur has the head of a bull but his body is human.

He is very cruel.
He likes to eat **children**!

Would you like to meet the Minotaur?

Sphinx (say *sfinks*)

The Sphinx has the head of a human.

She has the body of a lion, and the wings of an eagle.

She likes to talk to humans – then she eats them!

Quiz

Text Detective

- Which monster has only one eye?
- Would you like to meet any of these monsters?

Word Detective

- **Phonic Focus:** Final consonant clusters
  Page 3: Sound out the four phonemes in 'kind'.
  Can you blend the two sounds at the end?
- Page 4: Find a word that means 'very big'.
- Page 5: Find a word that rhymes with 'sings'.

Super Speller

Read these words:

who   kind   half

Now try to spell them!

HA! HA! HA!

Q What do you call monsters named Jon?

A Jonsters.

11

In this story

Pirate Jim

Captain Crab

Polly

The baby dragon

Tricky words

- dragon
- island
- where
- treasure
- tomorrow
- burn
- suddenly
- shook

Introduce these tricky words and help the reader when they come across them later!

Story starter

Captain Crab and his mate, Pirate Jim, live on a pirate ship called the *Donkey*. They are always searching for treasure. One day, Pirate Jim saw a baby dragon on an island. That gave him one of his **great** ideas.

Treasure Island

Pirate Jim saw a baby dragon on an island.

"Great!" he said. "Where there is a dragon, there is treasure!"

"Look!" said Jim. "The baby dragon has got a treasure box!"

"Come on, lads. Let's go and get it!" said Captain Crab.

The pirates landed on the island.
They crept up to the baby dragon.
"BOO!" they said.

The baby dragon jumped into
the sea and swam away.

The pirates got the treasure.
"Let's sleep on this island,"
said Jim. "Tomorrow we can
look for more treasure."

"Great idea!" said Captain Crab.
"Bad idea," said Polly.

It was cold on the island.
"We need a fire but there are no
trees to burn," said Captain Crab.

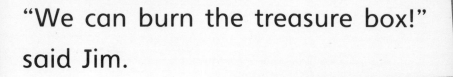

"We can burn the treasure box!" said Jim.

"Great idea!" said Captain Crab.
"Bad idea!" said Polly.

Do you think it is a good idea?

The pirates made a fire.
Suddenly, the island shook.

"Oh no!" said Jim. "This isn't an island. It is the baby dragon's dad!"

Do you think the baby dragon's dad is happy?

The dragon blew out the fire on his back, and he blew the pirates and the treasure into the sea.

The pirates swam, swam, swam away, and the baby dragon got his treasure back.

The pirates got away. But Captain Crab was cross with Jim.

"You and your great ideas!" he said. "Go to bed and *stay* in bed! You foolish boy!"

Quiz

- Why did the pirates go to the island?
- Why were there no trees on the island?

Word Detective

- **Phonic Focus:** Final consonant clusters
  Page 15: Sound out the five phonemes in 'crept'.
  Can you blend the two sounds at the end?
- Page 15: Why is 'BOO' in capital letters?
- Page 17: Find a word that rhymes with 'seed'.

Super Speller

Read these words:

crept   swam   blew

Now try to spell them!

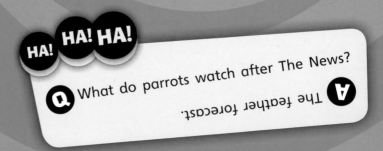

HA! HA! HA!

Q What do parrots watch after The News?

A The feather forecast.